a jazzy christmas

Wise Publications
part of The Music Sales Group
London / New York / Paris / Sydney / Copenhagen / Berlin / Madrid / Tokyo

Published by
Wise Publications
14-15 Berners Street,
London W1T 3LJ, UK.

Exclusive Distributors:
Music Sales Limited
Distribution Centre, Newmarket Road,
Bury St Edmunds, Suffolk IP33 3YB, UK.
Music Sales Pty Limited
20 Resolution Drive, Caringbah,
NSW 2229, Australia.

Order No. AM997810
ISBN 978-1-84938-125-3

Arranged by Paul Honey.
Processed by Paul Ewers Music Design.
Edited by Fiona Bolton.
Printed in the EU.

Images courtesy of istock / fotolia.

Your Guarantee of Quality
As publishers, we strive to produce every book to the
highest commercial standards.
This book has been carefully designed to minimise awkward
page turns and to make playing from it a real pleasure.
Particular care has been given to specifying acid-free, neutral-sized paper
made from pulps which have not been elemental chlorine bleached.
This pulp is from farmed sustainable forests and was
produced with special regard for the environment.
Throughout, the printing and binding have been planned to
ensure a sturdy, attractive publication which should give years of enjoyment.
If your copy fails to meet our high standards,
please inform us and we will gladly replace it.

www.musicsales.com

Contents

Performance Notes

Away In A Manger

A gentle jazz waltz, this tune contains reasonably long phrases. Equip yourself for these by taking deep breaths before the start of each phrase, enabling a strong sense of legato which will help the melody float over the accompaniment of the rhythm section. Also try playing the melody-line quavers with a very slight hint of swing.

Deck The Halls

It is of utmost importance that you keep to a steady tempo throughout this piece and do not succumb to the temptation to push ahead of the beat. This is particularly the case at the first entry of the melody in bar 9 when, given the absence of the piano, it is essential to lock in with the walking bass line. A similarly good sense of ensemble is also required in bars 17–20 when both you and the piano are playing the melody. Play out more during the solo section at bar 33 but remember to bring your volume back down at bar 49.

Ding Dong Merrily On High

This tune will benefit from a laid-back, almost throwaway sense of swing. Again, there are some long phrases and you should try playing each of the descending passages (bars 11–16, 19–24 and later, bars 59–64 and 67–72) in one breath. Good ensemble playing is also important in these bars as the piano joins you in playing the melody. At bar 35 it is in fact the piano that states the melody so think of yourself as providing an accompanying counter-melody at this point.

God Rest Ye Merry, Gentlemen

Work towards creating a marked contrast between the legato sections of this piece (such as bars 25–31) and the snappy, rhythmic passages that sandwich them. A similarly striking contrast should be created between the smooth minims and jazzy quaver movement in the solo section at bar 61. Pay careful attention to placing your notes with the rhythm section at bar 9 and once again, don't rush.

Hark! The Herald Angels Sing

This simple, gentle arrangement provides the perfect opportunity to display both controlled legato playing and increased emotion and expression. As in 'Away In A Manger', the classical, almost hymn-like melody should glide over the jazzy rhythm section, creating an effortless sense of contrast.

The Holly And The Ivy

Another jazz waltz to be played in a relaxed, almost lazy style. The quavers in this arrangement should be swung except in a few instances (such as bars 10–11 and 18–19). The extended solo section (bars 25–56) affords the opportunity to slowly build intensity, but ensure you return to the original relaxed feel when the melody is restated at bar 57, and play the last seven bars with a reflective feel.

Mary's Boy Child

This rumba-style arrangement requires you take the role of both soloist and accompanist. After stating the sprightly theme, bring your dynamic down to let the piano take over the melody (bar 37). However, do bring out the interesting quaver movement in bars 40, 44 and 48.

Mistletoe And Wine

Cliff Richard's 1988 Christmas hit, the first of his three singles to claim the Christmas No. 1 spot, is given a new twist in this cool jazz arrangement. Start the piece with a gentle tone, adding warmth to your sound as you reach the chorus (bar 21). Retain a relaxed feel even in the solo section, delivering controlled legato lines.

Silent Night

Resist the temptation to push ahead of the beat in this slow, thoughtful arrangement, especially during the solo section, to avoid giving the music any unwanted edge. Take deep breaths to see you through the long legato phrases and keep the dynamics fairly muted.

Sleigh Ride

Providing an opportunity to inject spirit and humour into your performance, there is plenty of scope to emphasise both the contrast between legato and staccato and the dynamic range in this Christmas romp; for example, bring out the crescendo at bar 37. The rhythm section switches to an 'in 2' feel in bars 57–64 and 73–80; highlight this by adopting a broader tone in these passages. Listen out for the sleigh bell entries and let them lift your performance.

We Three Kings Of Orient Are

Keep the rhythms tight in this up-tempo arrangement, and give the accented notes a little extra bite to create a sense of anticipation. Practise the tricky corners in bars 45–60 slowly, without the backing track, increasing the speed as your fingers become more comfortable with the quaver movement. Listen to the demonstration at bar 77 to inspire your own ad-libbed solo.

We Wish You A Merry Christmas

Another traditional carol given the fast-jazz treatment, this jaunty arrangement moves between a feeling of 'in 2' and 'in 4'. Listen carefully to the backing track at bar 27 in order to ground yourself at the start of the solo section when the piano is tacet. You can afford to add a dash of humour to your performance at the very end.

Away In A Manger

Words: Traditional
Music by William Kirkpatrick

Deck The Halls

Traditional

Ding Dong Merrily On High

Words by George Woodward
Music: Traditional

God Rest Ye Merry, Gentlemen

Traditional

Hark! The Herald Angels Sing

Words by Charles Wesley
Music: Traditional

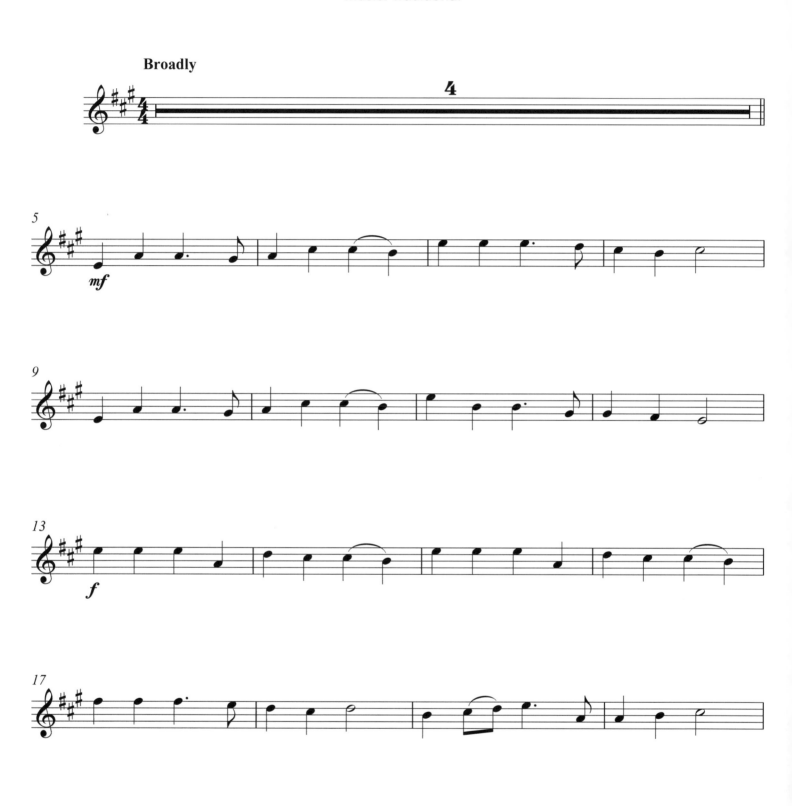

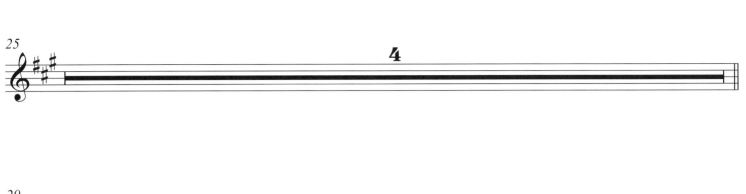

The Holly And The Ivy

Traditional

Mary's Boy Child

Words & Music by Jester Hairston

Moderate Latin Feel

Mistletoe And Wine

Words by Leslie Stewart & Jeremy Paul
Music by Keith Strachan

Silent Night

Words by Joseph Mohr
Music by Franz Gruber

We Three Kings Of Orient Are

Words & Music by John Henry Hopkins

Optional 8 bar ad lib. solo

rall.

We Wish You A Merry Christmas

Traditional

Sleigh Ride

By Leroy Anderson

1 2 3 4 5 6 7 8 9

a jazzy christmas

collect the series…

Your favourite carols and Christmas hits as you've never heard them before!

a jazzy christmas Book One

A unique collection of 14 great jazz arrangements for solo piano. Compiled and arranged by Paul Honey, this collection contains all your favourite carols as you've never heard them before! The songlist includes: *Away In A Manger, Deck The Halls, Ding Dong Merrily On High, Silent Night* and *We Wish You A Merry Christmas*. Each song is arranged for solo piano with chord symbols.

AM952919

a jazzy christmas Book Two

14 more fantastic jazz settings of Christmas favourites, selected and arranged for solo piano by Paul Honey. Includes: *All I Want For Christmas Is You, Jingle Bells, Joy To The World, Santa Baby* and *While Shepherds Watched*. Each song is arranged for solo piano with chord symbols.

AM997964

Play-Along Series…

Each with a CD of professional performances of every piece featuring a live jazz trio, plus backing tracks to play along with.

a jazzy christmas
Flute Play-Along
AM997755

a jazzy christmas
Clarinet Play-Along
AM997810

a jazzy christmas
Alto Saxophone Play-Along
AM997821

a jazzy christmas
Trumpet Play-Along
AM997832

a jazzy christmas
Tenor Saxophone Play-Along
AM997854

CD Tracklisting

1 Tuning Notes

Demonstration Tracks

2 Away In A Manger
(Traditional/Kirkpatrick)
Dorsey Brothers Music Limited.

3 Deck The Halls
(Traditional)
Brothers Music Limited.

4 Ding Dong Merrily On High
(Traditional/Woodward)
Dorsey Brothers Music Limited

5 God Rest Ye Merry, Gentlemen
(Traditional)
Dorsey Brothers Music Limited.

6 Hark! The Herald Angels Sing
(Wesley/Traditional)
Dorsey Brothers Music Limited.

7 The Holly And The Ivy
(Traditional)
Dorsey Brothers Music Limited.

8 Mary's Boy Child
(Hairston)
Bourne Music Limited.

9 Mistletoe And Wine
(Stewart/Paul/Strachan)
Patch Music Limited.

10 Silent Night
(Mohr/Gruber)
Dorsey Brothers Music Limited.

11 We Three Kings Of Orient Are
(Hopkins)
Dorsey Brothers Music Limited.

12 We Wish You A Merry Christmas
(Traditional)
Dorsey Brothers Music Limited.

13 Sleigh Ride
(Parish/Anderson)
EMI Harmonies Limited.

Backing Tracks

14 Away In A Manger

15 Deck The Halls

16 Ding Dong Merrily On High

17 God Rest Ye Merry, Gentlemen

18 Hark! The Herald Angels Sing

19 The Holly And The Ivy

20 Mary's Boy Child

21 Mistletoe And Wine

22 Silent Night

23 We Three Kings Of Orient Are

24 We Wish You A Merry Christmas

25 Sleigh Ride

CD Mixed & Mastered - Jonas Persson
Keyboards - Paul Honey
Bass - Don Richardson
Drums - Chris Baron
Alto Saxophone - Howard McGill

To remove your CD from the plastic sleeve,
lift the small lip to break the perforations.
Replace the disc after use for convenient storage.